HERBAL MEDICINE FOR DOGS

by Mary Boughton

Published by
Amberwood Publishing Ltd
Rochester, England

PLANTLIFE

Registered Charity No. 1059559
enquiries@plantlife.org.uk

Support Plantlife International, the wild plant conservation charity dedicated
exclusively to conserving all forms of plant life in their natural habitats in the
UK, Europe and across the world.

ISBN 1-899308-25-3

Cover design by Studio Read

Cartoons by Peter Read

Printed in Great Britain by Kent Art Printers who use
environmentally friendly production methods. The inks used have been
derived from a vegetable (not mineral oil) base, and the booklet has been
printed using "alcohol-free" dampening for dramatically reduced Volatile
Organic Compound (VOC) Emissions. The power used in the print
production of this booklet has been supplied by Ecotricity.

CONTENTS

About the Author

Mary Boughton was born and bred in West Dorset, where she lives with her husband Tony and children Roly and Joanna. The whole family is passionate about the countryside, its plants and animals and are actively involved in all aspects of rural life in this beautiful county.

She is a director of Dorwest Herbs Ltd, a rural business in which all four members of the family are involved. The company is based in Bridport, Dorset and has been producing and supplying veterinary herbal medicines and dietary supplements for dogs and cats since 1948. She has been involved in all aspects of the production of herbal medicines for over 35 years and is responsible for setting the Quality Control standards for all the company's activities.

Mary is a member of the British Herbal Medicines Association's Veterinary Committee and is Vice-chairman of the National Office of Animal Health's (NOAH) Companion Animal Sub-Committee.

She writes for veterinary and companion animal publications and lectures to veterinary practices, students and the general public on the use of herbal medicines and alternative therapies for companion animals and their place in modern veterinary practice.

About the Cartoonist

Peter Read is a freelance graphic designer and illustrator living in Penzance, Cornwall.

He studied for six years at Guildford School of Art. He qualified in 1960 and spent the '60s in London working in art studios and advertising. He became graphic designer for a French International cosmetic company.

In 1970 he went freelance. Illustration became more and more prominent in his work and the cartoon strips and illustration work with IPC Magazines gave him the opportunity of living and working down in Cornwall.

Dedication

To my parents and parent's-in-law who started it all off, to my husband, Tony, for his inspiration and enthusiasm for anything doggie and to Mr Tweed, a very special Border Terrier.

MR. TWEED.

Foreword

The treatment of animals has been used ever since man started to care for those that we invited into our homes. Initially these started as treatments that people discovered helped their own ailments after eating certain plants. Veterinary medicine has been recognised since the 17th-18th Century and commended for its approach to treatment by several great homeopaths when in the 18th-19th Century human medicine started to turn to toxic chemicals, bizarre purging and blood letting for relief. Both human and veterinary medicine has changed over the last century with many treatments being 'refined' from natural sources e.g. Aspirin from Willow, Penicillin from mould to name but two. These have in some respects brought about massive reduction in the suffering of the majority and combined with an increased understanding of the anatomy and physiology (the general workings of the mammalian body) many would say a massive improvement. However, in the wealth of discovery and science some knowledge and quality of the natural treatments, which were effective and used for centuries, have been almost overwhelmed and taken from us.

My inquisitiveness which first lead me into veterinary medicine, helped and guided by some notable colleagues, introduced me into the world of complementary therapies first through homeopathy and acupuncture. With this introduction, also came the most ancient of all medicines, the use of herbs. Several years ago this was what brought about my introduction to Mary. There are all sorts of herbal remedies available today and all sorts of people professing the activity of one over the use of another. It is always good to develop contacts with expertise and a wealth of knowledge in their field, to develop in them a source you can trust.

In all walks of life we make decisions on the basis of an 'experience cascade'. First and foremost based on our personal experience, and this has the strongest influence. If that experience is not available, then we will turn to the experiences of close family and friends (including our beloved pets). If, in turn, this is not available then we will turn to the experiences of those sources we should trust, for example doctors, vets and other professional colleagues. If, in turn, this experience is not available then we will turn to the reports of scientific papers, books and even newspapers. We are all individuals, even our pets, and what one person perceives is the right way may be perceived differently by another. It is wrong of us to dictate which decisions another person takes, but we should simply introduce another view to help that individual make that important decision. It is easy to be overawed by the claims and depth of feeling that comes with an individual's experience with any one product but caution should come with the use of novel and uncommon products, especially if they have not been 'tried and tested' in certain species. A good example of this in conventional medicine can be simply seen where people will gain symptomatic relief with paracetomol or ibuprofen – however, these can be deadly to a cat or dog respectively.

This book by Mary is a good introduction into the world of herbs as a complementary medicine to promote health and healing in our pets. It should suit both pet owners and conventional vets who wish to broaden their horizons and enhance their repertoire for helping the ailing patient.

Brendan Clarke BVetMed VetMFHom MRCVS

Note to Reader

1 | Introduction

I am so pleased to have been able to finally put together this small book on the use of herbs for both maintaining good health and treating common ailments in dogs. A book on the use of herbs for dogs has been sorely needed by pet owners and professional breeders for more years than I care to remember. The first such book I ever came across was a 1958 edition of 'The Complete Herbal Book for the Dog' by that most amazing and knowledgeable of ladies, Juliette de Bairacli Levy. It was the first book entirely devoted to natural rearing and the treatment of dogs using herbs and became the authoritative volume for generations of dog owners and breeders, having been revised and re-printed many times over the years. My husband and I were lucky enough to meet Juliette one evening in the early 1970's on the eve of Crufts Dog Show which was then held in Olympia. She was sitting on a dustbin waiting for friends but despite this somewhat ungainly seat, she had immediate presence and a great sense of fun and enjoyment of life. I shall never forget her bright twinkling blue eyes as I chatted to her throughout the course of the next few days. We felt privileged to have had the opportunity to talk to her and to gain from her the knowledge she obtained through her practical use of herbs for dogs and cats. I recall not only her sense of humour but also the fact that her knowledge was combined with a great deal of practical common sense.

I come from a background that is saturated in both animals and herbs – my parents were very involved in the use of herbs for treatments and cooking, so we grew the herbs and then used them for ourselves and our animals. Our household was vegetarian and only unprocessed wholefoods were allowed in our diets. This was quite unusual back in the 1940's when this approach to diet was relatively unheard of and thought to be extremely cranky. What a change we have seen since then! We always had dogs and cats in our home, as well as chickens, goats and various assorted other creatures that arrived and often stayed. In the late 1940's my parents started a business called Dorwest Herbs, which dealt in anything to do with herbs – plants, seeds, pot-pourri's and of course herbal medicines for people and their animals. Our company has now become the leading supplier of veterinary herbal medicine in the UK. It was when my husband, Tony and I got together in the early 1970's that the real specialisation into veterinary herbs began – his grandfather was a vet and his father a dog trainer, so their house was always full of dogs, dogs and more dogs. I owned, bred, showed and loved Cavalier King Charles Spaniels for over 20 years and Tony meanwhile has been involved in working dogs, particularly Lurchers and German Shepherds and he now also has a great interest in a number of the recently introduced rare breeds. We are a true family firm with now both of our children, Roly and Joanna, being the third generation to be involved. At home now we have a German Shepherd, a Scottish Deerhound and a Border Terrier as well as a cat and two breeds of bantam hens. Of course both Roly and Joanna are heavily involved with dogs as well and Roly has a working Lurcher while Jo has two show Whippets. With all these animals that we live and work with everyday, we all need a large herb garden to provide for them all!

2 | How to give herbs and herbal medicines to dogs

Herbs can be administered in many forms and which is best will depend on the breed of dog and the reason for giving it – as an addition to the diet or as a medicinal treatment. They can be given in various forms – freshly picked and chopped to a pulp, dried and powdered, as a liquid extract or purchased as a commercially produced tablet or capsule. Whichever way you choose to administer a herb, the most important thing to check is that you have the right plant and that it has not been contaminated. The herbs used to produce commercial medicines are tested for identity using thin layer chromatography and also to ensure that they meet the exacting specifications laid down in the British Herbal Pharmacopiea.

Most healthy dogs will eat their food greedily and so it is much easier to add finely chopped herbs, tablets and other forms of herbal supplements into their feed. However, if you are treating a specific condition when a set dose is required, it is always advisable to give this as tablets or capsules so that the correct amount is administered. There are only around 25 licensed veterinary herbal medicines for dogs and cats on the UK market. They are available for most common canine complaints and using these will guarantee the quality, safety and efficacy of the herbs and is by far the best way to ensure effectiveness. If a medicine is not available for a specific condition that you want to treat, then look for a supplement that has been manufactured by a reputable company where the quality and safety of the formulation will be assured. It is always advisable to give the daily dosage of the medicine divided into two or three doses throughout the day. This will help to ensure that a regular amount of the medication is in the system and so be more effective.

Many people are surprised to learn that commercially manufactured herbal medicines are subjected to much more stringent testing procedures than similar products manufactured for people. The reason for this is that we can choose for ourselves whether to take a particular herb or medicine, whereas an animal cannot. It is for this reason that it is only permissible by law for a qualified veterinary practitioner to treat an animal that is not their own – so don't try and treat other people's dogs and treat your own only when you are sure of what you are doing and what you are using.

–SO DON'T TRY TO TREAT OTHER PEOPLES DOGS.

3 | The quality of herbs used in medicines

Herbal medicine is more correctly called Phytotherapy and it has come a long way since the rather 'hit and miss' days of the past when it was only the skill and experience of the individual herbalist who could correctly identify a plant, even in a dried form, and know its properties. Checking the quality of the herbs used is vitally important because if the wrong herb is used or if it is contaminated or impure then the effectiveness of it in treatment will be reduced and it may even be unsafe to use for your dog. Nowadays, the whole field of phytotherapy has become more scientific, with herbs being identified and analysed using the benefits of modern science. Their effectiveness and therapeutic properties are also clinically tested and recorded. Perhaps this is the reason that many veterinary surgeons now are happy to use this form of treatment, either alone or in conjunction with orthodox medicines.

If you grow your own herbs or pick them from the wild, then you must be especially aware of pollution and contamination. Plants can be contaminated through the soil in which they are grown or from air and environmental pollution. Growing your own herbs is always preferable as you know exactly where the plant has come from, in which soil it has been grown and what has been sprayed onto it. I would hope that you would also want to grow your herbs organically to avoid any unwanted chemicals being retained in the plants. If you gather herbs from the wild then you must be particularly careful. Plants grown on roadside verges are likely to have been contaminated by exhaust fumes and those in fields may have been sprayed by chemicals; so think carefully before you pick. Even a site that looks ideal may have hidden dangers, so make sure that the ground wasn't formerly used as a landfill site, for example, as the soil might then be contaminated. Remember also that if you pick wild plants, you must never dig up the roots as these are protected by law, and only take what leaves or berries you need from the plant so it will be available again the following year.

4 | How do herbal medicines work?

Herbal medicines and other alternative forms of therapy, have generally become more and more popular over recent years. It is therefore not surprising that the interest in using them for our companion animals has also increased dramatically. The majority of people, including the veterinary profession, have all come to realise that these more traditional methods of dealing with health problems are not only effective for a whole range of everyday problems but also that they do not generally have the severe side-effects that can be so prevalent in some modern drug therapies. Of course, most of us are aware that many invaluable drugs were originally derived from plants and that synthetic versions are in everyday use. The advantage of synthesising the active ingredient from a plant is that it eliminates variation, removes any possibility of contamination and enables accurate administration. Those trained in the use of herbal medicine have long maintained that it is only by administering the whole plant in its natural form in the correct dose, that the worrying adverse reactions and long term side effects are virtually eliminated whilst the benefits are still appreciable, even if through their more gentle action, they may occasionally be slower to show results. The scientific testing now used to check the identity and purity of the herbs used in medicines has also meant that modern herbal medicines are made to the same standards as other pharmaceutical products and so can be used with confidence.

Many people confuse herbal medicine with homoeopathy and you will find that I have included some homoeopathic remedies which I have found useful. Nevertheless, homoeopathy and phytotherapy are two quite distinct forms of medicine and work in different ways. A simple explanation would be that homeopathic medicines are derived from a much wider range of ingredients than herbal medicines – using material of animal, vegetable and mineral origin. Minute dilutions of the active ingredient are used, which if they were introduced into the system at their full strength would actually cause symptoms similar to that from which the patient is suffering. However, when administered in these infinitesimal amounts they actually work in the opposite way and relieve the symptoms. This is where the homeopathic philosophy of 'like cures like' originates. By contrast, herbal medicine works in the same way as modern medicines, that is that herbs contain elements which have a direct physiological effect on the body. Virtually all medicines were originally based on herbs and plants. Herbal medicine has a long and well documented history. Until about the turn of the century these were almost the only medicines available, with the birth of 'modern' medicine being generally accepted with the discovery of modern antibiotics.

It is sometimes said that herbal medicine has a placebo effect, so if you think it is doing you good, then it will do so. For me, one of the most satisfying aspects of using herbs to treat dogs is that when the condition improves, it can only be as a result of the treatment given and not because the animal thought it would do them good! The treatment works because it is effective and not because the animal thinks it should, no matter how intelligent they are !

It is important to appreciate the basic differences between using herbal medicines for yourself and giving them to your pets. Dogs are carnivores and their systems are quite different to our own. This effects both the dosages they need and the form in which herbs should be given to be most effective. Carnivores are unable to digest cellulose in it's raw state and so cannot easily benefit from the chlorophyll in the plants given. Therefore any herb given to them must be in a form that they can absorb, usually finely powdered or pulped or an extract made from the plant. In the wild, carnivores will fulfil their need for the vitamins and minerals in plants by eating the partly digested, broken down plant material in the stomachs of their prey, and we need to simulate this in the herbal products we give them. Their digestive systems are much shorter than ours and so the herbs have to be absorbed in a much shorter time. Never assume that because a food, herb or medicine is good for you that it will also be good for your dog. This is a common fallacy and could have fatal consequences in some cases.

Plants and herbs have been used in all countries and cultures of the world for thousands of years, their use is well documented and is the basis of all forms of medicine. This does not mean that using herbal medicines for your dog will replace the skill and expertise of the veterinary surgeon which is always needed for any serious condition, so if in any doubt always take professional advice. Most herbs can be used in conjunction with modern orthodox medicines so there should never be a conflict between the two forms of medicine which can complement each other to the great benefit of your dog.

NEVER ASSUME THAT BECAUSE A FOOD, HERB OR MEDICINE IS GOOD FOR YOU THAT IT WILL ALSO BE GOOD FOR YOUR DOG.

5 | Foods as medicines and medicines as foods

Many foods are used as medicines and similarly many plants used as medicines are also common foods. Watercress, celery, parsley, garlic and even rhubarb are used in medicines as much as in foods. Of course many herbs used medicinally are plants that grow in the wild and many of the weeds that we all spend time trying to eliminate from our gardens – nettles, goosegrass, chickweed and dandelion are some of the most used plants in medicine. So what is a herb? Officially, it is a plant whose leaves are more aromatic than it's flowers, lavender, thyme, sage etc. but nowadays the term 'herb' tends to cover any plant that has a use in either cooking or medicine. So it is almost impossible to separate the foods we eat from the herbs we use in medicine. This is quite logical – all plants are made up of many thousands of complex chemical compounds and it is this mixture of compounds that we eat in our food and which are essential for health. We would not consider it healthy to eat our food as single chemical entities and it is this basis which forms the foundation of phytotherapy. It is the very diverse mix of chemical compounds in plants which provides the supporting or modifying effects and is thought to be the reason for the much lower instances of side effects. So the correlation between foods and medicines is as old as man itself and often the line between the two is difficult to define.

Dogs are carnivores and although over the centuries they have become adapted to eat most things, their systems are designed to eat and digest raw meat. Their digestive tracts are short and so they need high protein food which can be quickly absorbed. The recent trend for convenience complete foods is, in my opinion, as unnatural for the dog as the giving of meat products to cows and sheep. For good health any animal should be given the types of food that it's body is designed to deal with. So, the basis for a dog's diet should be good quality meat, preferably fed raw and in chunks or roughly minced. The best meats are tripe, chicken, lamb, beef and rabbit with fish being given occasionally. Because our domestic dogs are not able to obtain other nutrients from the partly digested stomachs of their prey, which they would have done in the wild, we have to simulate this by adding supplements and vegetables in a suitable form to make up a balanced diet. Finely chopped or powdered green herbs can be added to the feed and vegetables are beneficial as they also provide a good range of vitamin and minerals. Again, they must be broken down sufficiently to be absorbed and a juicer or blender is ideal for doing this. It will reduce the vegetables to a pulp and draw out the juices. Most root and leaf vegetables can be used and parsley, spinach, watercress and carrots are particularly nutritious. Potatoes and onions though are not recommended for giving to dogs.

Other additions should be made to the diet to deal with specific occasions in the dog's life as they occur – puppyhood, pregnancy, old age etc. and herbal treatments used for the common everyday complaints.

Owners always worry as to whether they are feeding a 'balanced' diet – why? Do we spend undue time worrying whether our own diet is balanced? We have all been persuaded that if we don't feed a diet to our dogs that contains all the added minerals and vitamins, we are failing as owners. Dogs are hunters and scavengers by nature and over thousands of years have become adapted to make very good use of their food. A good basic meat-based diet is the birthright of every dog and in recent years many problems have been recorded that are thought to be as a result of incorrect feeding of high protein cereal based foods. Only active working dogs need these high protein levels, the average adult family dog will be happier and healthier without them.

A word here about the recent trend of owners who are vegetarians or vegans to also feed their animals on this type of diet. Dogs can survive on a non-meat diet but it is totally unnatural and I consider it an act of selfishness on the part of any owner to force this diet on their dog just because they wish to follow a vegetarian diet themselves. I feel able to say this as someone who was brought up as a vegetarian in a vegetarian household at a time when this was not as fashionable or as accepted as it is today. Indeed, I would go further and say that it is as unnatural as giving cows or horses meat to eat and we all know now what problems that can cause. Give any dog a choice between fresh raw meat and a processed cube of food and you'll soon see which it prefers. Few of us would like, or consider it healthy, to be fed convenience processed foods everyday and nor do our dogs.

6 | Why don't more vets offer herbal treatments?

The veterinary profession have always tended to approach herbal medicines with scepticism and distrust. There is certainly more than one reason for this and it is worth considering some of these when looking at the place of modern herbal medicine. We are in an age when more and more people are using alternative therapies for themselves and demanding the same for their pets. Firstly and perhaps the most common cause for this mistrust is that most veterinary surgeons know very little about herbs, having had little training or instruction in the use of natural medicine or its place and relevance to modern day medicine. Veterinary colleges have now started to include this information as part of their courses and in recent years I have been asked to lecture to a number of veterinary and animal care students on the subject. This indicates just how much interest has grown in the whole field of natural treatments. Of course, most vets are aware that many invaluable drugs were originally derived from plants and that synthetic versions are in everyday use, but the added benefit of giving the plants in their whole form is not fully understood.

WHY DON'T MORE VETS OFFER HERBAL TREATMENT?

Another reason for the suspicion of herbal medicine is that many vets wrongly assume that those advocating this form of treatment expect it to be used for all diseases and conditions. Nobody would presume to ignore the need for surgical operations or to dismiss the plethora of effective modern drugs that are regularly and effectively used for conditions where no botanically produced alternative is or ever will be available. The majority of drugs are not now produced from botanic origins but they have proved their worth in treating many diseases that would have remained incurable in the past and this should not be forgotten. However, it does not mean that medicines made from plants should be ignored and dismissed as totally out of date. For many chronic but not life-threatening conditions they could, and perhaps should, be the first form of treatment having proved their worth over centuries of use. The two disciplines can and do work together, and not against each other, thus giving the owner and the dog the benefit of appropriate all-round treatment of disease.

Of course we as pet owners, albeit unwittingly, also have some responsibility for the lack of alternative treatments available from our local vet. When an animal is presented for treatment, the veterinary surgeon wants to treat it effectively and appropriately and we, the pet owner, often expect that a single visit and a short course of treatment will deal with the problem. This pressure to cure, also has a part to play in many vets reluctance to use herbal medicines. This expectation of the 'quick fix' is something that people have become accustomed to, probably since the introduction of antibiotics at the beginning of the twentieth century which are quick acting and so almost magical in their effects. Perhaps all of us, as pet owners, should reduce our demands and expectations and thereby allow our vets to use alternatives when appropriate, accepting that they may be slower acting but still effective. Licensed herbal medicines are among the range of treatments now available to vets and can be used with confidence – they are pure, safe, efficacious, of the highest quality and are appropriate for many of the common complaints that we visit our surgery for. Their great advantage has always been the minimal side effects and that after all is the one aspect of modern medicine that causes most concern and which we all want to avoid or minimise whenever possible.

There are now a growing number of homoeopathic vets and many of these also use herbs and other alternative treatments in their practices.

My experience however, is that when a vet embraces alternative or complementary treatments they tend to try almost anything and sometimes forget to think about where the herbs they use come from and the quality of them. I find it quite strange that we have on the one hand, old-fashioned orthodox vets who refuse to even consider using any complementary treatments and on the other an increasing number of holistic vets using almost anything regardless of its quality or if there is any data to support it. Hopefully, we will soon arrive at the situation where a middle way is achieved with all vets using a combination of modern medicines and properly authenticated and assessed herbal and complementary treatments.

At the present time we can only say that herbal medicine certainly has a place in the modern veterinary practice and more and more practices are using it in conjunction with other treatments. Properly assessed and manufactured herbal medicines are again regaining their traditional place in many surgeries for the treatment of a wide range of complaints. With more information, education and understanding of this old form of medicine it will perhaps soon be as widely available as it deserves to be.

7 | The herbs and their therapeutic properties

There are thousands of plants used in medicines and there is not space to list them all, but the following herbs are the most commonly used.

Celery ~ *Apium graveolens*

More often used as a vegetable than a medicinal herb, the seeds and also to some extent the leaves of this plant are very effective in reducing arthritic and rheumatic pain and this is their main therapeutic use. They are often combined with other herbs in either simple combinations or used as an active ingredient in manufactured herbal medicines. They can, however, be given on their own when they should be soaked in warm water for 24 hours and then mixed with the food on a daily basis. The odour is somewhat strong if they are given in this form and a prepared form would therefore be more acceptable for the smaller breeds of dogs. Celery also has a diuretic action which helps in eliminating toxins from the system as well as keeping the kidneys functioning properly.

Chamomile ~ *Matricaria recutita*

There are many species of this plant but this variety, also known as German Chamomile is the most often used medicinally and it is the flowers that are used, normally as a tea. There are two main properties that are of use for companion animals as well as for people. Chamomile is wonderfully soothing and cleansing for the digestive tract and soothes upset tummies, as everyone who has read Peter Rabbit will already know! In many European countries, even today, Chamomile tea is the first drink given to babies after birth to cleanse the digestive system, which illustrates just how gentle and safe it is. I have used this for young puppies and also

*'CHAMOMILE' - IDEAL FOR PUPPIES WITH STOMACH UPSETS
THROUGH OVEREATING, ESPECIALLY THINGS THAT THEY SHOULDN'T!*

gave it to my children regularly when they were young. Even now they are grown up, they drink it if they are feeling unwell, although nowadays they have to make their own! Secondly, Chamomile is a mild and gentle sedative and is very useful to relieve the pain of teething as well as aiding sleep. It is ideal for puppies who suffer from stomach upsets through overeating, especially things that they shouldn't ! Chamomile flowers are well known for their beneficial effects on the hair and are often incorporated into shampoos. Combing the tea through the dog's coat will also be beneficial and it is particularly good for paler coated dogs such as Golden Retrievers.

Clivers ~ *Galium aparine*

Known by most of us as Goosegrass, this is a plant which we are so used to see climbing up our hedgerows that we may tend to overlook its properties. It is an effective diuretic and because of this is useful for skin conditions as it helps cleanse the system. It's blood purifying properties assist in removing toxins. Clivers is rich in chlorophyll and in the Springtime the fresh plant can be gathered, chopped and added to feed occasionally as a useful addition to the diet.

Comfrey ~ *Symphytum officinale*

Whole books have been written on this herb which has so many properties and medicinal uses that it would be impossible to list them all without devoting an entire book to the subject. Both the root and the leaves are used medicinally and probably its main use for dogs is its ability to aid the healing of fractures, sprains and swellings. The leaves can be used externally as a poultice by boiling them in a very little water, allowing it to cool and applying this to the affected area for about 20 minutes, securing it in place with a dressing. After this time, remove it and replace with a few bruised leaves which can remain in place until the following day when another poultice can be applied in the same way. The herb should also be given internally to aid the healing process and this is best administered in tablet form or as the homoeopathic remedy Symphytum 15C. In 1993 as a result of research carried out on various species of the Comfrey family, concern was expressed because the plant contains pyrrolizidine alkaloids which may pose a threat to health. Despite the fact that there have been no conclusive links to illness in people, and certainly none at all in dogs, it was recommended by the UK's Food Safety Directorate and the Veterinary Products Committee that Comfrey root should not be taken internally and the leaves not for prolonged periods. There was a perceived risk that if large quantities were taken internally over a long period it might result in health problems. Of course, as far as dogs are concerned, it is extremely unlikely that large enough amounts of the herb could be taken internally and even then the lifespan of these animals makes it almost impossible for them to live long enough to suffer any ill effects. Comfrey is largely now used either externally, which is perfectly safe, and internally only for short periods during treatment. This means that although it is always wise to be aware of the situation, this scare should cause little concern to those wishing to obtain the considerable benefits of this herb for their dogs. Comfrey is extensively used both internally and externally in the treatment of horses.

Cornsilk ~ Zea mays

I always think that the very name conjures up softness. Cornsilk is the name given to those fibres consisting of the styles and stigmas that lie between the sweetcorn that we eat and the protective sepals. When you buy corn on the cob you invariably throw them away whilst preparing the vegetable but they are invaluable for cystitis and to sooth the urinary tract generally. Steep them in boiling water, leave to cool and give a quarter pint or so of the resulting liquid three or more times a day to help reduce the effects of cystitis and other urinary conditions. A cheap and very effective remedy that works for people as well as animals.

Couch grass ~ Agropyrum repens

This may be the scourge of gardeners, but its rhizomes are also one of the most widely used medicinal plants for it's diuretic properties. It helps to keep the kidneys functioning well and is used for cystitis and other urinary tract problems. It is often mixed with other diuretic herbs and can be given as a tea although it is probably best administered in a proprietary form. One of the things that owners always worry about is why their dog eats Couch Grass leaves, particularly during the Springtime when it is young and succulent. Some dogs seem to almost graze amongst this grass and people always wonder why they do this. It has been said that they are eating it because they 'know what is good for them', but this is very unlikely as dogs gain little benefit from the grass which is very rough and coarse and generally passes straight through them without digestion. Often the dog will eat the grass, then vomit it up along with some bile and then go straight back and do the same again. Basically, this is exactly the reason for eating the grass. It is not that the dog is really ill, but it is feeling in need of cleansing and detoxifying it's system and eating Couch grass to make itself vomit is it's way of helping to remove toxins from the system. If your dog does this on a regular basis, try fasting it one day a week and so enable it to rest it's digestive system and you'll find that it will not feel the need to eat Couch grass quite so often. In any case, it is absolutely nothing to be concerned about as it is not a symptom of severe illness but simply the dog giving itself a Spring clean! See the section on vomitting under the problem section later in the book.

Dandelion ~ *Taraxacum officinale*

Another herb which is so widely known and recognised that it needs no description and one which was until recently still listed in the *British Pharmacopœia*. Although both the leaves and root are used medicinally it is leaves that can be gathered easily, chopped finely and added to the diet to provide minerals and vitamins and also act as a good tonic for the liver. It is probably best known medicinally as a diuretic and so very useful for the older dog to maintain good kidney function.

Elderberry ~ *Sambucus nigra*

All parts of the Elder tree are used in various ways, but it is the berries which are rich in iron, iodine and Vitamin C and so are particularly good for improving and maintaining pigmentation in dogs. In the Autumn when the berries are abundant, pick the bunches, strip the berries off the twigs and loose freeze them to use later on in the year. Then once or twice a week during the Winter, simply defrost a teaspoonful or so and add to your pet's meal. Many dogs like to eat Blackberries too, and the same can be done with these. I have owned a number of dogs who picked these for themselves off the bushes and obviously loved the flavour.

Evening Primrose ~ *Œnothera biennis*

Recently the oil of this plant had become so popular that even orthodox vets are using it on a regular basis in their practices. The active part of the oil is the gamma linolenic acid and for best effect when giving to dogs, the level of this should be at least 10%. The oil promotes good coat growth and seems to help prevent excess shedding. For this reason it is widely used by owners of the long coated breeds of dog to grow those wonderful coats seen in the show ring. Studies have shown that the oil also has mild anti-inflammatory properties and so will also benefit a scurfy, itchy coat if the condition is not too severe when it will be necessary to use a stronger herbal combination. Many people are aware that Evening Primrose Oil has been found helpful in regulating hormonal imbalances.

For this reason it is a very useful addition to the diet for bitches after having pups to aid the hormones to return normal. However, Evening Primrose Oil should not be given to dogs who suffer from epilepsy as, along with other volatile oils, it has been known to induce fits.

'EVENING PRIMROSE'—WIDELY USED BY OWNERS OF THE LONG COATED BREEDS OF DOG TO GROW THOSE WONDERFUL COATS SEEN IN THE SHOW RING.

Fenugreek ~ *Trigoinella Fœnum-Græcum*

Perhaps best known as an ingredient in curry spices, it is the seeds of the plant that are used. It has been extensively used externally in poultices to treat abscesses and sores, but is more often used internally. Fenugreek has antiseptic properties and for this reason is very effective when combined with Garlic, each having a synergistic effect on the other. Given in larger quantities, Fenugreek will increase the appetite and has been used traditionally to help increase weight so can be given to dogs who need to gain body weight. Two tablespoons of the seeds should be soaked in half a pint of warm water and left for 24 hours, a quantity of both the liquid and seeds, from a teaspoonful to a tablespoonful, depending on the size of the dog, should then be added to the daily feed.

Garlic ~ *Allium sativum*

One of the most commonly used and effective plants , often called 'the king of herbs' for this reason. It is the essential oil that contains the properties of the plant. Although raw garlic is beneficial added to the feed, it is more effective for treatment to give it in tablet form so that sufficient quantities of the oil can be easily administered. Garlic capsules are not as suitable as tablets for veterinary use as the Garlic oil is mixed with a carrier oil to bulk the size of the capsule and this carrier oil is not always beneficial for dogs. Garlic has antibiotic, antiseptic and anti-viral properties, so can be used both externally and internally for treating minor infections. During the First World War, before modern anti-biotics were available, Garlic was widely used to treat the wounds of soldiers at the front, being one of the most effective treatments available at that time. It removes toxins from the body, increases resistance to infection by stimulating the immune system and is well known for its ability to help maintain a healthy heart and circulatory system. Specifically indicated for coughs and other upper respiratory conditions, its antibiotic action also means that it is used extensively for a wide range of skin problems that affect dogs. It has a strong and pungent odour which also makes it effective in repelling fleas, lice and worms. Garlic is absorbed into the system very quickly and can be identified in the urine within 15 minutes of being given internally! As we all are aware, giving too much garlic can make the motions loose but if this should occur it will only be temporary and if a lower dose is then given and the quantity gradually increased it is usually very well tolerated. One thing that some people worry about is whether they can give Garlic along with homoeopathic remedies as there are those who say that strong smelling or tasting foods can effect the remedy. Following a great deal of research and many conversations with the most eminent homoeopathic vets in the UK, I can assure you that this is not the case and Garlic can be safely given with homoeopathy, indeed one leading vet I spoke to regularly uses Garlic tablets along with homoeopathic treatment with good results. Another story about Garlic which has recently been circulating, mainly via the internet, is that garlic should not be given to dogs or cats as it can cause anaemia. There is absolutely no truth in this and no data to support it. This is confirmed by the fact that veterinary medicines containing garlic have been manufactured and supplied for over 50 years. As licensed medicines, any suspected adverse reactions or side effects have to be recorded and reported to the UK government medicines authorities. There have been none reported at all. I am certain that during the 50 years that they have been so widely used and all the documentation that there is on them, that it would soon have been picked up if there was a problem or if there was any truth at all in this. Where these rumours start from and who starts them is a mystery but over the years that I have been involved in herbal medicines there have been many of these 'scare stories' put about and rarely do they have any substance in fact.

Hops ~ *Humulus lupulus*

There must be very few people who will not have experienced the properties of this plant, as any beer drinker will testify! It is the volatile oil in the plant that produces the sedative and soporific effects that we are all accustomed to occasionally. Use it with care when giving to pets as it may make them sleepy.

'HOPS' - USE IT WITH CARE WHEN GIVING TO PETS!

Marigold ~ *Calendula officinalis*

This flower is familiar to everyone as a cottage garden plant and is one of my favourites. The flowers and leaves can be used internally but perhaps it's most common use is in balms, lotions or ointments containing the flowers. This is soothing for wounds and grazes and has wonderful healing properties.

Mistletoe ~ *Viscum album*

This plant is often thought of only as a traditional Christmas decoration but it has a fascinating history and is a potent medicinal herb. It grows abundantly in France, from where most commercially used Mistletoe is obtained. Its use in various rituals goes back to pagan times and its medicinal actions were well known by our forebears. It is the leaves and stems that are used medicinally and not the berries which are poisonous. Mistletoe is a strong nervine, used to calm and relax. It is a component in proprietary herbal medicines for small animals where it's use is valuable for conditions ranging from anxiety to epilepsy. An interesting and valuable herb that is extremely useful in small animal treatments.

Nettle ~ *Urtica dioica*

The common stinging nettle is a much maligned plant with an interesting background. It is reputed to have been introduced into Britain by the Romans but no-one is sure whether this was accidental or intended. It seems more likely that it was intentional as among other uses nettle leaves can be eaten as a vegetable and made into beer. Nettle soup is one of the favourite recipes in our house and always on the menu every Spring when the leaves are young and tasty. The stringy stems were used for making cloth, paper and sewing thread as recently as the first half of the 20th century. It also has a range of medicinal properties mainly due to the presence of formic acid, a wide range of mineral salts, phosphates and iron in its leaves. The cooked leaves, chopped finely, are an excellent source of chlorophyll and iron and can be added to the dog's feed where they will not only provide minerals in the diet but are useful in the treatment of skin disorders and rheumatism. The leaves can also be made into a tea and combed through the coat to add shine and help remove scurfiness. All in all, this is a wonderful herb which fortunately is easily available and recognised by everyone.

Parsley ~ *Apium petroselinum*

For such a commonly used herb, it is amazing to find that there are so many superstitions and traditions centred around it. It's use goes back to the Greeks where it was highly valued and used for a whole range of conditions. Nowadays it is mainly for its diuretic properties that it is used but it is another of the green herbs which can be chopped and added to the diet to provide vitamins, keep the breath sweet and help prevent overheating and its associated itchiness.

Pennyroyal ~ *Mentha pulegium*

This is both the smallest and also the strongest smelling of the mint family. The oil that is present in the leaves helps to repel fleas and was used for this as far back as Roman times. A tea using 1 oz. leaves to 1 pint of water can be used as a final rinse after bathing your dog during the Summertime when parasites are at their most troublesome. The leaves can also be bruised and rubbed into the coat or try using a shampoo containing Pennyroyal extract – your dog will smell gorgeous too!

Raspberry leaves ~ *Rubus Idæus*

Known for centuries as a tonic for the reproductive organs. Giving Raspberry leaves, either finely chopped, as a tea or in tablets, helps ensure easy whelping. It should be given from the third week of gestation and carried on until one week after the birth to help prevent the retention of afterbirths. Of course, nothing other than medical intervention will help in some cases, such as when a large puppy becomes stuck in the birth canal, but for bitches who have previously had normal but prolonged labour, Raspberry leaf has proved it's worth time and again over the years. I took it myself during pregnancy for both of my children, so can vouch personally that it works for people too! Unfortunately some bitches are prone to phantom pregnancies and they often occur season after season. Whereas spaying the bitch may be the only long-term answer, giving Raspberry leaf at double the normal amount from the first sign of the bitch coming into season and carrying on for 12 weeks, will usually prevent a phantom from developing. Raspberry leaf can also be used for a wide range of reproductive problems, although veterinary advice should be sought if there is a persistent discharge or the dog has a high temperature, as this could indicate an infection such as pyometra that will need immediate veterinary treatment.

Rosemary ~ *Rosmarinus officinalis*

This plant is not really suitable for adding to the feed as it is rather strong smelling. However, Rosemary contains a strong volatile oil that has antiseptic properties and has many external uses for dogs. A simple tea made using 1oz. leaves steeped in 1 pint of boiling water, allowed to cool, strained and used as a coat rinse will put a wonderful shine on dark coats and will also deter fleas and other parasites that dislike its strong smell.

Rue ~ *Ruta graveolens*

One of the most bitter and sour smelling herbs in the garden – either loved or hated depending on individual taste. It is popular with flower arrangers because of its attractive grey foliage and its nickname of the 'herb of grace' comes from its traditional use in religious ceremonies. It has many medicinal properties but for the dog owner its most valuable use is to hang it in bunches together with Wormwood or Pennyroyal, in or above the dog's bed to help deter parasites and flies.

Sage ~ *Salvia officinalis*

Too common to need description this herb is grown in most kitchen gardens. It is antiseptic and the leaves can be rubbed on the teeth and gums to clean and whiten the teeth as well as keeping the gums healthy. It is also included in some veterinary toothpastes. Another useful tip is to chop and soak a few leaves in hot water, allow it to cool, add honey and use the resulting strained liquid to relieve sore throats – fortunately as this is an evergreen herb the leaves are available for this remedy throughout the Winter months for both us and our dogs.

'SAGE' IS INCLUDED IN SOME VETERINARY TOOTHPASTES.

Scullcap ~ *Scutellaria laterifora*

The old country name for this herb is 'mad dog weed' due to its reputation for use in dogs with hydrophobia or rabies. Fortunately, I have no experience of the results of this particular claim, but it certainly possesses strong nervine and anti-spasmodic properties and so has a valuable place in herbal medicine as a very reliable remedy. It is particularly suitable for dogs as it will calm and relax without causing drowsiness or any unpleasant after effects. It can be used for any occasion when anxiety, nervousness or a phobia is a problem but it is also used for convulsions, epilepsy and other similar conditions when it is normally combined with other herbs or used in conjunction with orthodox anti-spasmodic drugs.

Seaweeds

There are a number of seaweeds that are incorporated in animal feedstuffs but the finest seaweed, and the one to use medicinally, is Kelp (*Fucus vesiculosus*). This has a high mineral content, contains all 37 minerals and trace elements and is therefore a good basic addition to the feed as a way of ensuring all the necessary minerals are in the diet in a form that can be readily absorbed. Due to its high iodine and iron content Kelp stimulates coat growth and maintains good pigmentation. If given from Autumn onwards throughout the Winter, it will encourage thick coat growth and help to prevent the fading of eye and nose colour that sometimes occurs during the Winter. It has long been known that Kelp balances the metabolism and is therefore useful for regulating weight. It is normally given as a fine powder but if being used for treatments then tablet form is preferable. It is not advisable to give Kelp to an animal with a thyroid disorder without veterinary advice as the high level of iodine may be inappropriate. Similarly, if a dog has a skin problem or is hot and itchy then it is advisable not to give Kelp until the condition is better because the high levels of minerals may tend to overheat the system.

Slippery Elm ~ *Ulmus fulva*

It is the bark of this tree, native to North America, which is the part used medicinally. It is ground to a fine powder and is often mixed with other tree barks to make a mix which is extremely useful for a wide range of digestive problems from colitis and diarrhoea to pancreatic insufficiency and acute absorptive disorders. It is low in fat and salt but highly digestible and very nutritious and so makes a wonderful addition to the milky feeds given when weaning puppies. When the bark combines with the digestive juices it becomes mucilaginous and lines the whole digestive system, so slowing down the passage of food and firming the stools. It can be sprinkled onto the daily feed or mixed with liquid as required and should be in every dog owners First Aid box for helping those occasional bouts of diarrhoea or upset tummies. It is essential to use pure Slippery Elm powder and not be tempted to use it when diluted with flour, as this will not be so effective. As a child, I remember being given this when I was ill and subsequently used it for my own children when they had sickness and diarrhoea. So, as with many herbs, this can be used for all the family members whether two or four legged.

Tea Tree Oil ~ *Melaleuca alternifolia*

This oil which is extracted from a native Australian bush has in recent years become incredibly popular because of its antiseptic properties. It is incorporated in a number of shampoos, creams and lotions for external use. It should never be used in it's neat form as it is extremely strong and can burn the skin badly, so only use it when it is diluted in a properly produced commercial product. There have also been recent reports of dogs collapsing after Tea Tree Oil has been used so it must be used with great care.

Valerian ~ *Valeriana officinalis*

It is the root that is used extensively in herbal medicine and it is one of the herbs listed in the *British Pharmacopœia*. It is a powerful nervine and antispasmodic and is usually administered as an extract or combined with other herbs in tablets for veterinary use. It has a wonderful effect in calming the nervous system and reducing anxiety but has none of the after effects that a chemical tranquillizer may have such as drowsiness, red eyes etc. Valerian is used internally and often combined with other tranquillising herbs. Care should be taken not to give too much, so it is best to use it in a commercially prepared medicine where the dose will be regulated and correct for your dog.

Watercress ~ *Nasturtium officinale*

More commonly used as a salad herb, this plant is fortunately available all the year round nowadays and so the leaves and stalks can be finely pulped and added to the feed. Watercress is particularly rich in iron and Vitamin C as well as a wide range of other mineral salts. It helps to cool the system and so is beneficial for dogs prone to overheating.

Wormwood ~ *Artemesia absinthium*

Due to its strong antiseptic and anthelmintic properties, Wormwood has been included in a number of preparations for animals over the years. It is an intensely bitter herb and so is often used in combination with other herbs when given internally. Because of the unpleasant odour which comes from the volatile oil, the whole herb is disliked by parasites of all kinds and the fresh or dried leaves can be used to keep flies away and included in pet's bedding to deter fleas.

8 | Some common problems and how herbs can help

Allergies

In recent years, cats and dogs seem to have become more sensitive to a wide range of substances that they come into contact with, either in the environment or through their food. Dogs appear to suffer from food allergies more than cats and in these cases changing to a natural feeding regime, to reduce the additives given, has proved helpful. For contact allergies the only real way to solve the problem is to identify the cause and restrict the animal's access to it, although this can prove difficult in practice. It seems increasingly common that when no other cause can be found for a problem, especially a skin problem, it is designated an allergy – but this doesn't make it any easier to deal with! Many food allergies in dogs show themselves as a skin irritation and these are best treated using Garlic to deal with the infection, combined with the green leaf herbs to cool the skin and reduce the irritation. A combination of any of the following will be helpful – Parsley, Watercress, Horseradish, Lettuce, Dandelion, Celery or Nettle. Garlic juice can be applied to skin if there are sore places as it's antiseptic properties will help to stop infections while allowing the air to still reach the skin and so dry up any sore places. A cream or ointment containing Marigold (Calendula) or Lavender can be used to aid the healing and soothe sore places.

Anal Gland (inflamed)

The anal glands are on either side of the dog's anus and can easily become inflamed or blocked, particularly in the smaller toy breeds. The first signs of this are the dog dragging its bottom on the ground or continuously licking the area. It is essential that the diet contains enough roughage but that the motions are not too soft so that the glands are cleared by the pressure of faecal evacuation. Give a good wholemeal biscuit and Garlic internally to help prevent infection. Consult your vet if the problem persists or worsens as in extreme cases an absess can form. He will clear the anal glands manually, after which the area can be bathed with liquid Garlic.

Appetite (poor)

This is often a sign that a dog or cat is "off colour" or coming down with an illness, and so should be closely watched for symptoms of any developing illness. Healthy dogs should eat their food with enthusiasm but some are fussy eaters and must be encouraged to eat regularly. Although it may seem hard, do not be tempted to give titbits or attempt hand feeding. To help an adult dog to regain its appetite and eat enthusiastically again, the following regime should be effective. Start with a 24 hour fast using a gentle herbal laxative, followed by a small meal of just a quarter of the normal quantity and add a teaspoonful of Kelp Seaweed powder to stimulate the appetite. All this should be eaten eagerly as the dog will be feeling hungry but if the food is refused, remove the bowl and do not offer any more until the next mealtime – this alone often works like a charm. When the first meal has been taken, gradually increase the food at each meal, until normal sized meals are being eaten eagerly. It is worth remembering of course that a lack of appetite can be due to a serious condition and so if a dog goes off it's food for more than a few days you should consult your vet for a thorough health check.

Appetite (coprophagia or depraved appetite)

There are thought to be three possible causes of this unpleasant habit where dogs eat their own or others faeces. It may be as a result of feeding a processed dry diet, especially one which contains strong flavourings and may pass through the system unaltered. Changing to a more natural diet is therefore advisable and the addition of grated raw Carrot or Pineapple chunks are also helpful. Another cause can be boredom, especially in the case of younger dogs and those in kennels – regular exercise and companionship will help to keep the dog occupied and less likely to start this habit. The third possible cause is a lack of minerals in the diet, and in this case supplementing the feed with a good all round herbal mineral supplement will ensure that all the necessary minerals and trace elements are given. As this problem can easily become a habit, particularly in young dogs, it is essential to keep both the dog's housing and runs scrupulously clean and take steps to correct this problem swiftly.

Arthritis

While this condition cannot be cured, herbal treatment in conjunction with the correct diet will relieve the pain, make movement easier and help to delay the progress of the complaint. Although gentle exercise is beneficial for mobility it can be painful and should always be gentle and somewhat restricted. Diet is important and, as with people, the main things to avoid are red meats and dairy products which seem to aggravate the condition. While looking at the diet, also remember that if your dog is overweight this will lead to more stress being put on the arthritic joints. If your pet needs to lose weight, there are a number of commercial diet foods available, or more simply just cut down on the amount of food you give. Add Kelp seaweed to the food throughout the dieting period as this will not only help with weight loss but due to it's high mineral content it will make sure that during the diet there are enough minerals to keep him or her healthy. The herbs that will help relieve arthritis are Garlic, Celery seeds, Parsley and also Dandelion. They help to remove toxins that may have built up in the system and also relieve the pain and make movement easier. Remember that this condition will have developed over a long period of time and improvement will therefore be gradual. As improvement is made the amount of herbs given can be reduced. In the case of an older dog it is often necessary to continue this for the rest of the animal's life to prevent recurrence. Giving Cod Liver oil as a supplement during the Winter months is also useful, being naturally rich in Omega 3 fatty acids as well as Vitamins A and D, it does seem to also aid joint mobility.

Bad Breath

This is usually caused by teeth and gum disorders so have this checked and if necessary any decayed teeth should be removed by your veterinary surgeon. Regular brushing with a specially formulated veterinary toothpaste will help to keep the teeth and gums healthy. Sage is a wonderful herb for the gums as it is antiseptic and has disinfectant properties. It is incorporated in some veterinary toothpastes but also the bruised fresh leaves can be rubbed on the teeth and gums. Bad breath can also be caused by a digestive disorder and there are various herbs that can help with this – Ginger, Parsley, Rhubarb, Valerian and Peppermint are all good for settling the stomach and combinations of these herbs can be given in small quantities or in a prepared form. Garlic has antiseptic and antibacterial properties which will help to ensure that the digestive tract is kept healthy and free from harmful bacteria. The addition of fresh fruit and vegetables in the diet also helps sweeten the breath and most dogs love to have them occasionally.

Bladder and Kidney Disorders

As there are many serious, as well as minor bladder and kidney disorders it is advisable to consult your veterinary surgeon over these problems. Certainly if the condition persists or the animal's temperature is high professional advice should always be sought. However, giving herbs to keep the kidneys functioning well is always a good policy and the following are mildly diuretic and help to maintain a good urinary flow. Parsley, Dandelion, Couch grass and Clivers all have a diuretic action, are easily available and can be pulped or finely chopped and added to the daily feed.

Coat, dull or with scurf

A dull or thin coat is often the first outward sign of a drop in general condition and so if this is noticed then first check that there is not a more serious problem such as worms that may be the cause. A thinning or dull coat can be the first symptom of a hormonal or adrenal condition so it is always a good idea to consult your vet if you are concerned. Coats often become dull prior to the moult and a good grooming regime will help to remove this old dead coat and also stimulate the skin. This is particularly necessary in the Springtime when the Winter coat is being shed. Make sure that the dog has a good diet as this will be reflected in the coat and adding a small amount of Wheatgerm oil to the food occasionally will help put back that shine. In the Autumn when all animals start to grow a thick coat to protect them from the cold in the Winter, it is a good idea to add Kelp seaweed to the feed and this can be given either as tablets or powder to stimulate coat growth. For the long coated breeds, giving a good quality Evening primrose oil with a minimum of 10% gamma linolenic acid, will promote good quality coat growth, rectify dryness and improve skin condition. If you have Elderberries growing in your garden or nearby, then pick them in the Autumn and freeze them for use during the Winter. They are rich in iron and iodine and will help put a healthy shine on the coat as well as improving pigmentation. An old fashioned tip that works well, particularly for the dark coated breeds is to comb an infusion of Rosemary herb or cold tea through the coat occasionally, both of these will put a wonderful shine on the coat, and Rosemary repels parasites and also smells lovely and fresh!

Colitis

Some breeds of dog seem to be particularly prone to this condition more than others and it is very worrying for both dog and the owner. The first consideration is to find a diet that suits the animal and this can often be a matter of trial and error although white meat diets are generally better tolerated. The feeding of the meat and cereal foods at separate mealtimes is certainly also a good idea as it is less likely to cause fermentation in the digestive system and the awful possibility of bloat. One of the most effective herbs to use for this is pure Slippery Elm powder, which is made from the bark of the red elm tree, native to America. If available, powdered white Poplar bark and Marshmallow root can be add to this for an even better combination. Adding a small amount sprinkled on each feed has proved to be very helpful for animals with colitis. It is very nutritious, increases food toleration and by lining the digestive system it improves absorption and enables the dog to gain full benefit from its food. Many years ago Slippery Elm food, which contained a small amount of the herb mixed with flour, was a popular remedy for diarrhoea and to settle upset tummies, but it was not nearly so effective as using the pure powder which is a wonderful thing to keep on hand for all types of digestive upsets. I used this for my children when they were small and suffered from childhood bouts of diarrhoea and vomiting by making it into a warm milky drink, sweetened with honey. I remember being given this by my mother when I was a child, so it really is a traditional remedy in our family!

Constipation

Occasionally dogs can suffer from constipation but if this occurs regularly the first thing to look at is the diet. It is important to make sure that it contains enough roughage to prevent this. For mild constipation, or simply regular hard stools, giving garlic regularly is often all that is required, but for more stubborn cases giving a herbal laxative designed for dogs will alleviate the situation. However, if it persists for more than a day or two you should always consult your veterinary surgeon. The laxative herbs include Senna, Cape aloes, Cascara and Dandelion. A word here about giving bones – these should *always* be given raw as cooked bones may splinter and cause severe problems. Always give large bones, preferably marrowbones to dogs as they can enjoy chewing away at them for hours and it provides wonderful exercise for their teeth and gums. Some dogs are so keen on these that they crunch the bone up completely, which is not a problem in itself as their stomach acids are designed for this, but if the dog is not used to regularly eating bones or gets too carried away and eats too much, it can form a ball of powdered bone which can be difficult to pass and may even cause a blockage. If this happens, you will usually need veterinary attention after which it is a good idea to watch that the dog either doesn't get too enthusiastic with it's bones or give them on a more regular basis in small quantities in future.

Coughs and bronchial conditions

There are many different types of cough and it is not always possible for the owner to know whether this is serious or not. One of the most common causes is when something has become lodged in the throat and unless it is easy to see the cause, you should get professional help to remove it. A cough that is dry and unproductive may be an indication of a heart problem and again a visit to your vet will be required. Sometimes, a cough can simply be as a result of dogs barking excessively and again giving Garlic along with a soothing syrup of Blackberry or Rose-hips will help to clear this up. Kennel cough is one of the potentially most serious and also infectious causes of a persistent cough. It is caused by a virus called Bordella and as its name suggests can spread quickly from one dog to another if they are in close proximity. The virus will clear up of its own accord in time but often the vet will prescribe antibiotics to prevent any secondary infections. However, it is has been reported time and again that dogs which have garlic, particularly when combined with fenugreek seeds, in their diet regularly either raw or as tablets, seem to have an increased resistance to contracting this virus. As it is so infectious, dogs should be isolated if they contract kennel cough and giving garlic and fenugreek in large doses will aid recovery. However, if your dog has a persistent cough accompanied by a high temperature, veterinary help should always be sought. Occasionally dogs can suffer from hoarseness or a sore throat just as we can. Providing you are sure that this is not caused by anything more serious you can use Sage tea which is very soothing. Simply chop a few leaves of fresh Sage very finely and add a small quantity of boiling water in the same way that you would make tea. Let it cool, strain it and add a little honey to make it more palatable and there you are – a simple home remedy which works just as well for people as pets.

Cuts, Bites and Scratches

The treatment needed will depend on the severity of the problem. For minor scratches and cuts, clean the area well and use liquid Garlic or another of the antiseptic plants to prevent infection. An ointment containing Marigold or Tea Tree will be useful to soothe and heal the skin. For more severe cuts or bites, stop any bleeding by applying a cold compress and take your dog to the veterinary surgeon as soon as possible. Meanwhile, if you have homoeopathic Arnica 15C in your first aid box, give this to help reduce the effects of shock or trauma that may accompany such an injury.

Cystitis

If an animal is passing urine more frequently than normal and in small quantities, it may be that bladder inflammation or cystitis is the cause. There are a number of herbs that will soothe the situation – Clivers, Parsley, Dandelion, Couch grass root and Cornsilk, all increase the flow of urine and help to make it less acidic and painful. Also give Garlic, preferably in tablet form to ensure sufficient strength, to help fight any infection. It's important that the dog drinks plenty of water to help flush the kidneys and for this reason dry foods should be avoided as they tend to aggravate the situation. If the condition persists, if there is blood in the urine or a high temperature you should obtain veterinary advice as a more serious condition may be indicated.

Diarrhoea

This is nature's way of cleansing the body and unless persistent or accompanied by vomiting it should be allowed to run its course, if possible. Give a mild laxative to help it on its way and also Garlic or one of the other antibiotic herbs to clear up any infection that may be the cause. Fast for 24 hours and then gradually introduce food in small quantities to start with but remember never to give milk or dairy products until all symptoms have disappeared. Slippery Elm bark sprinkled on the food is highly digestible and soothing to the digestive system so can be given both during and in the recovery period following acute diarrhoea. However, it is important to consult your veterinarian if this condition persists for more than a few days. The homoeopathic remedy Merc Viv 15C is very effective in quickly stopping diarrhoea and so should be in every dog owner's First Aid kit.

Ear Problems

Some breeds of dog are very prone to ear problems, especially those with dropped ears where the air flow is restricted. Regular cleansing is essential and wiping the outer ear with Garlic juice or a specially prepared veterinary ear lotion will clean them very effectively. If there is a discharge or the ears are smelly the homoeopathic remedy Hepar Sulph 30C is very effective. When I owned Cavalier King Charles Spaniels, I used to use a clothes peg to put their ears together on the top of their heads at meal times, just catching the hair and not the flesh of course! This not only kept their ears out of their bowls but also allowed air to get to the ears for a short period every day and did seem to help avoid the problems that many spaniels suffer from because of their floppy ears.

Epilepsy

All cases of epileptic fits should be treated only in consultation with a veterinary surgeon, not only for diagnosis but also in order that the animal's condition can be monitored. There are herbal medicines especially for small animals that are licensed for use in the treatment of epilepsy and your vet will be able to advise you about these. Sometimes they are able to control the condition on their own but more often they are given in conjunction with the orthodox anti-spasmodic drugs. By combining the treatments it is often possible to reduce the quantity of drugs required to control the condition and also therefore the side-effects that are often experienced from epileptic drugs. Each sufferer will have a different pattern of fits so it is essential that veterinary advice is sought.

Excitability

Over-enthusiasm and excitability should not be considered a problem. This excitable behaviour is often found in young dogs and can sometimes make day to day living difficult for the owner, although often the situation will resolve itself with age and maturity. Taking your young dog to a local dog training class will help it to become better socialised and well behaved. You can use the tranquillising herbs, Scullcap, Valerian, Hops etc. to help to calm and relax dogs when excitability becomes a problem or a herbal licensed medicine that contains a combination of these. This will help the dog to concentrate more when being trained as well as being useful for those occasions when they can just get too over excited. Hyperactivity can be associated with an allergy to certain foods and food colourings in the same way that this can affect some children and changing to a more natural feeding regime is advisable.

OVER-ENTHUSIASM AND EXCITABILITY SHOULD
NOT BE CONSIDERED A PROBLEM.

Eye problems

There are a number of herbs that can be used in an eye-wash but I do not consider it is a good idea to actually put anything into the eye unless you know exactly what you are doing, are certain it is sterile and have been advised by a veterinary surgeon. One of the useful herbs to brighten the eyes is Eyebright (*Euphrasia officinalis*) but I suggest that you use this in the homoeopathic form, Euphrasia 15C, which is given internally. This is effective for many eye conditions, particularly for sticky or sore eyes when there is a discharge. If an eye condition lasts for more than a few days it may be that there is an infection and you should then also give Garlic tablets in fairly large quantities for a period of a week – if this doesn't clear up the problem it will probably require antibiotics from your vet.

General Condition

Good health and condition is something all dogs should have naturally. There are three basic essentials – adequate exercise every day and this should include a period of free running if possible. A dog running freely and at full stretch across a field is lovely to see and the way they enjoy it is evident. Companionship and good manners are a must – dogs have been domesticated for centuries and love human company and of course if they are trained to be well behaved everybody is much happier. A healthy diet is the third essential and a diet based on fresh raw meat with wholemeal cereal is still the best in my opinion. This should be supplemented with a variety of herbs and vegetables to add vitamins, minerals and other elements to provide a naturally balanced diet. Any of the green leaf herbs can be used, Parsley, Watercress, Dandelion leaves etc. but they must be either finely chopped, pulped or ground so that they are easily assimilated. Similarly, vegetables should be processed through a juicer or blender. The other daily supplements are Garlic for its protective qualities and Seaweed powder for its mineral content. This will keep dogs in good general health, although other supplements can be added to help specific problems and herbal medicines that have been especially formulated for animals, used to treat the minor problems that will inevitably occur at sometime in your dog's life.

Incontinence

As dogs get older they can suffer from bladder weakness and may pass urine more frequently and often in small quantities, sometimes without being aware of it. This can be very distressing for both them and their owners. There are a range of herbs that have diuretic properties, Parsley, Dandelion and Clivers being the most easily available, and if these are added to diet this will usually improve the situation and make the animal more comfortable by helping to ensure that the bladder is emptied completely when they urinate. If the condition persists then a vet's advice should be sought.

Indigestion

Although not a common problem in animals, some breeds are prone to it and attention to the diet is vital. There are a number of herbs that can help with this – Peppermint, Chamomile and Ginger are well known and will help to settle the stomach, aid digestion and reduce flatulence. Giving cereals and meat together in the same meal can cause fermentation which aggravates the problem, so dividing the daily food into two or three meals, giving cereal and meat separately, is advisable for dogs who have a delicate digestion.

Insect Bites and Stings

Young dogs seem to love chasing after insects and unfortunately this often means that they inadvertently may occasionally get stung, often in their mouths. This can potentially be very serious as not only can the mouth and throat swell up restricting the airway but there is also a real risk of anaphylactic shock. For this reason if your dog has been stung in the mouth always get him to a vet as soon as possible. For bites or stings in other places, clean the site of the injury, give the homoeopathic remedy Urtica Urens 30C but again if in any doubt, consult your vet.

Interdigital Cysts

These are small swellings between the toes and can be difficult to clear up as they have a habit of recurring. Firstly, make sure there are no foreign bodies in the area as often the cause is simply grass seeds which have lodged in the paws, especially in the Summer when dogs are running through long grass. Bathe the area with Garlic juice to clean it and give Garlic in large doses or tablets to clear up any infection. This treatment should be continued until the cysts have completely disappeared. Dogs who suffer from these cysts are usually prone to them recurring, so continue giving Garlic daily in the diet to help reduce the likelihood of further outbreaks.

Nervousness

There are many causes for a dog being nervous – thunder, fireworks, strangers and other similar things can all affect a nervous animal. There is sometimes a hereditary factor as well but the most common reason for this is perhaps poor socialisation at an early age. Dogs who have been regularly handled by people and met lots of other animals and come across a wide range of different situations are more likely to cope with those incidents that may make others nervous. Unfortunately, if the owner is nervous this is transmitted easily to the animal, so it is essential to behave in a confident and encouraging manner at all times. There are a number of herbs which will help to relax and calm your dog and therefore increase its confidence – Scullcap, Mistletoe, Valerian, Chamomile and Gentian are but a few that can be used. Every dog is an individual and so the length of time that treatment will be needed will vary depending on the severity and individual circumstances. The advantage of using herbal treatment to overcome situations where an animal may be nervous is that they generally will not make the dog drowsy or 'knock it out' completely as orthodox medicines often do.

Obesity

Incorrect feeding and lack of exercise are the most common causes of this familiar problem, seen so often in pet animals nowadays. As well as effecting the heart and circulation, obesity also puts extra strain on the joints leading to further complications. The first thing to say is that it is essential not to give titbits between meals. Reducing the amount of food given is the simplest way to aid weight loss but there are also several ready-prepared low calorie foods on the market that can help. Give Kelp

Seaweed in powder or tablets as well throughout the period. This has a high iodine content and so assists weight loss as well as providing a wide range of essential minerals. Make sure that the dog receives vitamins and trace elements by also adding a variety of green leaf herbs and vegetables to the daily feed. This will help to maintain full health and condition while weight reduction is being undertaken. Regular daily walks are essential but don't overdo it to begin with. We've all seen overweight dogs being dragged unwillingly out for a walk and while they may need some encouragement to begin with if they are not used to it and haven't had much previous exercise, this must be introduced gradually as fitness is built up, especially if other conditions such as arthritis are present or if the dog is elderly.

'OBESITY' – INCORRECT FEEDING AND LACK OF EXERCISE ARE THE MOST COMMON CAUSES OF THIS FAMILIAR PROBLEM.

Pancreatic Insufficiency

Some breeds of dog, especially German Shepherds, are more susceptible to this condition and it is something that should be treated in conjunction with your veterinary surgeon as the severity can vary from case to case. However, there are certain foods which are helpful in compensating for the maldigestion that results. A diet that is low in fat and salt and is highly digestible is essential and white meats do seem to generally be better tolerated. However, if you find a food that seems to suit your dog and is helping to control the problem then it is best to stick to it rather than change the food continually. One of the most effective herbs to add to the diet, by sprinkling it on the feed, is powdered Slippery Elm bark which will help to soothe the digestive system, slow down the passage of food through the system and so enable the dog to obtain the full benefit from its food. It can be safely given indefinitely in cases of chronic exocrine pancreatic insufficiency and is also useful to have on hand for occasional bouts of diarrhoea.

Phantom Pregnancy

This tiresome condition is fairly prevalent in dogs. It is as much a psychological problem as a physical one. Unfortunately bitches that have a tendency to phantom pregnancies will often suffer season after season and ultimately it may be necessary to have the bitch spayed to prevent further episodes. However, for various reasons you may not wish to take this measure without pursuing other options first. There is one thing that has proved helpful to many bitches by either preventing them having a phantom or reducing its effects. Raspberry leaves have long been given to pregnant animals, and people, to help an easy birth. However, it has been found that giving it daily from the first sign of the bitch coming into season and continuing for twelve weeks, which is up to the time when she would have whelped had she been mated, seems to reduce dramatically the chance of her having a phantom pregnancy. Some bitches get very stressed and anxious at this time and so the herbs that reduce anxiety can also be given to keep her calm and relaxed. If the worst happens and the symptoms of a phantom pregnancy do occur, try giving the homoeopathic remedy Pulsatilla 15C which is often effective in reducing the symptoms. If she starts to produce milk as well, then Urtica Urens 3C will help.

*'PHANTOM PREGNANCY' – THIS TIRESOME CONDITION
IS FAIRLY PREVALENT IN DOGS.*

Pigmentation

The pigmentation problems that people mainly worry about, especially in show dogs, is when a drop in pigment causes a pale nose or eyes and this often occurs in bitches after a season or pregnancy and more often during the Winter months. The fading is thought to be due to a lack of minerals in the diet, particularly iron and iodine although there may be other causes. To help maintain pigment during the Winter months always make sure you give Kelp seaweed powder or tablets from Autumn through to Spring. If pigment has already been lost or needs improving try adding Elderberries and Nettles to the feed or use a commercially prepared liquid extract or tincture. Both these plants are rich in iron and iodine, although the Nettles must be gently cooked to remove the sting before adding to the animal's food! Keep this up for at least two months to help regain the previous good pigmentation. If you are lucky enough to have an Elderberry tree in your garden, pick the berries in the Autumn, freeze them and add a dessertspoonful to the feed every day throughout the Winter. A word of warning, however, if you notice a drop in colour of the gums always consult your vet as this may well indicate anaemia and depending on the severity it may require veterinary treatment, or may be a symptom of a more serious condition.

Rheumatism

As with people, this is more common in the older dog or cat and the first signs are usually stiffness when getting up after sleeping or exercise and it is difficult to distinguish from arthritis without X-rays being taken. Fortunately, the herbal treatment for both arthritis and rheumatism is broadly similar. There is no real cure for these conditions but life can be made easier for the sufferer, the pain reduced and mobility increased. The herbal treatment and diet suggested for arthritis should be followed and this can be continued safely for the rest of the dog's life. This will reduce the pain, make movement easier and it is often the case that the dog appears to take on 'a new lease of life'. At this stage in their lives most elderly animals appreciate the comfort of a warm dry place in which to settle down as the damp, cold weather does seem to make the symptoms worse. Keeping your dog warm and dry during the Winter months and being careful to dry him off after being outside are also good precautionary measures. Cod Liver oil has become popular to aid mobility and is worth adding to the diet during the Winter months in any case because of its high levels of Vitamins A and D.

Showing

There are many reasons for problems in the show ring but the most common seem to be either as a result of a bad experience or rough handling in the ring or simply young dogs who may be apprehensive when they are not quite sure what is expected of them. Naturally, it can be a bit over-awing for a young dog to find itself surrounded by lots of others and crowds of people if he's not used to it. This can make him feel unsure and therefore unable to show at his best. It is essential to give a lot of encouragement and to instil confidence in your dog, so always remember to act confidently yourself. Training and ring craft classes are the best way to get the dog used to all the hub-bub of the show ring but if despite this they still need a little something to settle their nerves, then give one or more of the tranquillising herbs Scullcap, Valerian, Mistletoe or Chamomile. These are best given in liquid or tablet form and ideally should be administered about two hours before going into the show ring. Given in the correct quantity, they won't have any adverse effects or causing drowsiness so can even be given to dogs doing obedience work and field trials. As the young dog gets more used to the experience he will usually take it in his stride and nearly all dogs look forward to going to shows and really enjoy their showing careers once they mature.

Sexual Behaviour

We've all heard tales of male dogs behaving badly and so the story goes it's always when the vicar comes to tea! This actually happened to us when the vicar arrived one day, so I can vouch personally for the fact that it is a true story and very embarrassing indeed. The sex drive is very strong in some male dogs and certainly can sometimes be unacceptable to us as owners. There is not a lot that can be done and the best advice is to move the dog to another room when the vicar arrives! Sometimes having the dog castrated will reduce the sex drive, but this is certainly not always the case, so consider this before having surgery. The homoeopathic remedy Gelsemium 30C does help to reduce sexual behaviour and so is useful to have on hand for such occasions. This is especially useful to give in a situation where a bitch in season nearby is causing your dog to become extremely excitable.

'SEXUAL BEHAVIOUR'—WE'VE ALL HEARD TALES OF MALE DOGS
BEHAVING BADLY AND IT'S ALWAYS WHEN
THE VICAR COMES TO TEA!

Shock or Trauma

The first remedy to reach for when dealing with the result of any shock or trauma is homoeopathic Arnica 15C. If the trauma is a result of an injury or accident it will be especially useful as this remedy helps to stop bleeding, aids healing and reduces bruising. It is therefore an essential item to have on hand for emergencies to use while you are waiting for the vet to arrive. In this situation it should be given every 15 minutes until help comes.

Skin Complaints

There are many types of skin problems and some are difficult to clear up, although they can usually be controlled effectively. First check that there are no fleas, lice or other parasites present, and also that the condition is not caused by your dog having picked up mange. Mange mites burrow deep into the skin and so are difficult to diagnose and to remove. There has been a great increase in mange in recent years which I am certain is partly due to the number of foxes, both rural and urban, coming into our gardens, from where the dog then contracts the mites. There are both homoeopathic and other alternative ways of dealing with mange but personally I prefer to use orthodox veterinary treatment for this to make sure of completely getting rid of it, so my advice is to use your vet if you think mange may be the cause of a skin problem. However, the most common types of skin conditions are dermatitis, eczema, pyoderma, or a non-specific allergy condition, often known as 'overheating' which is particularly common in some breeds, especially terriers. The symptoms are typified by inflamed hot skin and itchiness often with some bald patches resulting. While this itchiness is not actually caused by hot weather, it does tend to be more obvious in the Summer time when the warmer weather can aggravate an already hot skin. Similarly this is often noticed in the Autumn when we switch on the central heating in our homes. So being aware of external heat and how it can affect skin problems is obviously very relevant if your dog is prone to overheating. It is important to try and deal with the cause and therefore first you should consider your dog's diet. For adult dogs change to a plain, simple diet giving only white meat or fish with the addition of boiled rice to provide the cereal content and treat with herbs to cool the skin and fight any skin infection. Usually after one month a good quality biscuit meal can be introduced and other items very gradually, although this will depend on the improvement made. Avoid high protein foods, red meats, vitamin and mineral supplements and of course titbits! To treat the condition and reduce the irritation, give Garlic for it's antibiotic and antiseptic properties and also the green leaf herbs, especially Parsley, Watercress, Spinach, Mint, Nettles and Celery to cool the skin and reduce the urge to scratch. Keep strictly to the diet and add good quantities of the herbs, or a combination in tablet form, for at least a month and then reduce the amount as the condition improves. When the skin irritation is stabilised it is sensible to make sure that susceptible animals continue to have these green leaf herbs in the diet to help prevent the system from overheating. Evening primrose oil is also a helpful supplement to give to maintain a healthy skin and it will also encourage new coat growth, so is very beneficial if there has been coat loss

Sprains, strains, fractures etc

Obviously fractures must be treated by a veterinary surgeon but the homoeopathic remedy Symphytum 15C should also be given to aid the healing process. Being prepared from Comfrey herb it is no surprise that it is also beneficial for sprains, damaged cartilages, tendons etc. Comfrey leaves and root can also be used as a poultice externally so a good supply of these in your garden is very useful. See the section on Comfrey for details of how to prepare the poultice. Working and running dogs are more likely to suffer from sprains and strains for when this occurs the prime healer is rest with just minimal exercise. Give Symphytum 15C for a period of 10 days and if the dog is frustrated and stressed through being somewhat confined, then give the calming herbs of Scullcap, Mistletoe, Valerian and Vervain to help it relax while its body heals. Always seek veterinary advice if there is swelling or heat in a joint or if no improvement is made within a fortnight.

Travelling and Car Journeys

The main travelling problems are either nervousness or excitability, particularly in young dogs. Regular short journeys, with lots of encouragement, from an early age will help enormously. It's best not to give a meal before travelling, but instead give calming herbs to reduce anxiety. This will also reduce excessive salivation during the journey by keeping the dog calmer and less apprehensive. If your dog really can't get used to the car then there are a number of tips that I've found useful – put his bed or blanket in the car when it is stationery and leave him there to sleep for short periods during the day; try feeding him in the car or sitting in the car with him with the engine running but no motion. All these things will help your dog realise that this is not quite so frightening as he thought and get him used to accepting the car as part of his environment. While travelling some dogs prefer to be able to see out of the window, some find it easier if they can't see out, so there are no hard and fast rules, try everything and see what helps your dog most. For dogs who are not nervous when travelling but suffer from real motion sickness, give powdered Ginger, Peppermint or Chamomile to aid digestion and a little Valerian to settle the stomach. Real motion sickness needs to be dealt with as quickly as possible as otherwise the dog may become nervous about being in the car and then you may have two problems to deal with.

'TRAVELLING AND CAR JOURNEYS' – WHILE TRAVELLING SOME DOGS PREFER TO BE ABLE TO SEE OUT OF THE WINDOW.

Vomiting

Dogs will often vomit after grass eating and although this seems to worry owners, it is certainly no great cause for concern. They particularly love couch grass and eat it as a way of cleansing and detoxifying their systems. It is rough and coarse and so encourages them to vomit. It seems that they know when their system needs this and they suffer no ill effects from this practice. They will often bring the grass back up with a little bile, although sometimes it passes through the system with no problems. Give Wheatgerm Oil, either as liquid or capsules, and Garlic to help with the detoxifying process and also Ginger, Chamomile or Peppermint to help settle the stomach. It is worth noting that dogs who have a regular once a week fast day, to rest their digestions, rarely feel the need to eat grass to cleanse their systems. This is something we have always practised with all our adult dogs and they soon get used to the idea if it is done regularly. Prolonged or persistent vomiting will require veterinary attention, but if this is not immediately available, give the homoeopathic remedy Arsenicum Alb 30C, which for this very reason should be in your pet's first aid kit. It is particularly affective if the vomiting is accompanied by diarrhoea or is the result of suspected food poisoning.

Whelping

There are many unexpected problems that can occur during pregnancy and whelping, although most breeds of dog should be able to deliver their pups without problems. There are lots of books to advise the pet owner on what to expect and how to deal with the birth but your local veterinary practice should be kept informed of the expected delivery date in case their help is needed. There are some bitches who have previously given birth naturally but have had to cope with a normal but prolonged or unduly extended labour. For these cases, giving Raspberry leaves, either as a tea or tablets, from the third week after mating until one week after delivery will strengthen the reproductive system and aid the birth. Many normal easy births have taken place following the use of this traditional birth remedy. During labour itself give the homoeopathic remedy Caulophyllum 30C to help ease the birth, but if in any doubt at all always seek veterinary assistance immediately.

9 | Dog and cat owner's first aid kit

There are certain things that you should never be without and keeping a pet first-aid kit is the best way of making sure you know where things are when you need them in a hurry. Here are the things I find useful –

Herbs

- Tablets containing a combination of Garlic, Fenugreek or Wormwood to treat minor infections.
- Veterinary tranquillising tablets containing a combination of Scullcap, Mistletoe, Valerian or Vervain.
- Liquid garlic juice for cleaning wounds.
- Herbal laxative tablets or powder.
- Slippery Elm powder for diarrhoea and upset tummies.

Homoeopathic remedies

- Arnica 15C for shock, trauma, bruising and bleeding.
- Arsenicum Alb 15C for vomitting with diarrhoea.
- Gelscmium 30C for oversexed males.
- Merc Viv 15C for diarrhoea.
- Urtica Urens 30C for insect bites.

10 | Useful addresses and contacts

The Kennel Club
1 Clarges St, London W1Y 8AB
Tel: 0870-6066750
www.the-kennel-club.org.uk

The British Association of Homoeopathic Veterinary Surgeons
The Alternative Veterinary Centre, Chinham House,
Stanford in the Vale, Faringdon OX7 8NQ
Tel: 01367 718243
www.bahvs.com

Association of Pet Behaviour Counsellors
PO Box 46, Worcester WR8 9YS
Tel: 01386-751151
www.apbc.org.uk

British Herbal Medicine Association
1 Wickham Road, Boscombe, Bournemouth BH7 6JX
Tel: 01202 433691
www.bhma.info

Recommended Food suppliers

Meats

Anglian Meat Products
Unit 1–2 Threxton Road Ind Estate, Watton IP25 6NG
Tel: 01953-883770

Forthglade Ltd
Bellinster Factory Estate, Berners Cross, Winkleigh EX19 8DH
Tel: 01837-83322

Wholemeal biscuits

Natural Choice Ltd
4 Withiel Drive, Cannington, Bridgwater TA5 2LY
Tel: 01278-652184

Fenlife Ltd
London Road, Dunchurch, Rugby CV23 9LR
Tel: 01788-810283

'INITIATIVE'

Veterinary herbal medicines and supplements
Dorwest Herbs Ltd
Shipton Gorge, Bridport, Dorset DT6 4LP
Tel: 0870 7337272
www.dorwest.com

Denes Natural Pet Care Ltd
2 Osmond Road, Hove BN3 1BR
Tel: 01273-325364
www.denes.com

Herbs and where to get them

Your local supplier or health food shop
Powdered Ginger, Chamomile flowers, Fenugreek seeds, Celery, Dandelion leaf, Evening Primrose oil, Garlic, Kelp seaweed, Mistletoe, Nettle leaf, Raspberry leaf, Sage leaf, Skullcap, Slippery Elm, Valerian, Wormwood etc.

Herbs to grow in the garden
Parsley, Sage, Comfrey, Rosemary, Catnip, Rue, Wormwood, Marigold.

Wild herbs to pick with care
Elderberries, Dandelion, Clivers, Nettles.

Other specialised herbs are best used in an extract or tablet form manufactured for veterinary use.

'RECREATION'

OTHER BOOKS from AMBERWOOD PUBLISHING:

AROMATHERAPY

Aromatherapy – A Guide for Home Use by Christine Westwood. £1.99.
Aromatherapy – For Stress Management by Christine Westwood. £3.50.
Aromatherapy – A Nurses Guide by Ann Percival. £2.99.
Aromatherapy – A Nurses Guide for Women by Ann Percival. £3.50.
Aromatherapy – Simply For You by Marion Del Gaudio Mak. £2.99.
Aroma Science – The Chemistry & Bioactivity of Essential Oils by Dr Maria Lis-Balchin. £5.99.
Aromatherapy – Essential Oils in Colour by Dr. Rosemary Caddy. £9.99.
Aromatherapy – The Essential Blending Guide by Dr. Rosemary Caddy. £12.99
Aromatherapy Lexicon – The Essential Reference by Geoff Lyth and Sue Charles. £4.99.
Aromatherapy – The Baby Book by Marion Del Gaudio Mak. £3.99
Aromatherapy – The Pregnancy Book by Jennie Supper. £5.99

HERBAL

Ginkgo Biloba – Ancient Medicine by Dr Desmond Corrigan. £2.99.
Echinacea – Indian Medicine for the Immune System by Dr Desmond Corrigan. £2.99.
Herbal Medicine for Sleep & Relaxation by Dr Desmond Corrigan. £2.99.
Garlic– How Garlic Protects Your Heart by Prof E. Ernst. £3.99.
Phytotherapy – Fifty Vital Herbs by Andrew Chevallier. £6.99
Natural Taste – Herbal Teas, A Guide for Home Use by Andrew Chevallier. £3.50.
Woman Medicine – Vitex Agnus Castus by Simon Mills. £2.99.
Menopause – The Herbal Way by Andrew Chevallier. £5.99
Herbal First Aid – Natural Medicine by Andrew Chevallier. £3.50.
Plant Medicine – A Guide for Home Use by Charlotte Mitchell. £2.99.
Cancer – Herbs in Holistic Healthcare by Dr J. Walker. £15.99.
Herbal Medicine for Children by Frances Hambly. £6.99.

GENERAL HEALTHCARE

Insomnia – Doctor I Can't Sleep by Dr Adrian Williams. £2.99.
Eyecare Eyewear – For Better Vision by Mark Rossi. £3.99.
Arthritis and Rheumatism – The Sufferers Guide by Dr John Cosh. £4.95.
Feng Shui – A Guide for Home Use by Karen Ward. £2.99

NUTRITION

Causes & Prevention of Vitamin Deficiency by Dr L. Mervyn. £2.99
Vitamins ABC and Other Food Facts (for Children) by E. Palmer. £3.99
All You Ever Wanted To Know About Vitamins by Dr Leonard Mervyn. £6.99.

CALL FOR INFORMATION: **(01634) 290115**